LIFE
IN THE OCEANS

LIFE
IN THE OCEANS

Text and Photographs by
NORBERT WU

HARCOURT BRACE & COMPANY

Orlando Atlanta Austin Boston San Francisco Chicago Dallas New York
Toronto London

This edition is published by special arrangement with Little, Brown and Company (Inc.).

Grateful acknowledgment is made to Little, Brown and Company (Inc.) for permission to reprint *Life in the Oceans* by Norbert Wu. Copyright © 1991 by Tern Enterprise, Inc.

Printed in the United States of America

ISBN 0-15-305235-X

8   9   10   060   99

Dedication

To my parents, whose love and support have allowed me to realize my dreams.

Acknowledgements

This book is a distillation of many shared experiences, and the photographs in it would not have been taken without the help of the following people.

Thanks to Deanna for her endless patience and loving care, Alberta and Lance for being there.

My diving buddies have been the best, and I specially thank Howard Hall, Marjorie Bank, and Marty Snyderman for their advice and help through the years. The many folks at Our World-Underwater helped me jump-start my career, and Mark Conlin, Spencer Yeh, Sam Shabb, and Andy Day have braved many a day of cold waters with good humor. Maggie Geoghagen of the *Caribbean Explorer,* Fritz Falkner of the *Pacific Nomad,* and Curly Carswell of Sea Fiji put their belief in my work and treated me to some great diving. Arnold Griessle and the staff at Tan/Sahsa Airlines, and Julie King and staff at Hawaiian Airlines, were most helpful in arranging transportation to various destinations.

At Scripps Institution of Oceanography, Peter Breuggeman deserves a round of applause for his enthusiasm and attention to the state of the library, as do Dr. Richard Rosenblatt, H.J. Walker, and Cindy Klepallo for their help with the Marine Vertebrate Collection. Dr. Richard Harbison and Ron Gilmer helped me through five weeks of Arctic blue water diving, and Dr. Ken Smith and his crew helped me with another five weeks of diving in the Central North Pacific.

C O N T

E N T S

INTRODUCTION

A diver moves along a coral wall in the Caribbean, with sea fans in the foreground. Coral reefs often have sheer cliffs of coral which plunge to great depths. A profusion of life covers these walls, which are formed by uncountable numbers of coral polyps building and exuding their limestone skeletons, one on top of the other, generation after generation.

Think of how long three hundred feet is. It's the length of a football field. A man can run that far in under ten seconds. Good players can throw a Frisbee™ that far. Normally three hundred feet is not considered a significant distance. Yet under the ocean, three hundred feet is a huge distance. The sun's light is so weak at this depth that no plant life grows, and divers are happy if they can see things as far as 100 feet away. Scuba divers hardly ever go deeper than half this depth, and even that distance is considered dangerous. At 300 feet, scuba divers cannot breathe regular air mixtures, because the intense water pressure turns oxygen poisonous.

The average depth of the oceans

is 13,000 feet (over two miles), therefore only a very tiny part of the world's oceans has ever been seen by man. Because the oceans are still largely unexplored, little is known about the behaviors and habits of ocean creatures. Only recently have tremendous ridges, rifts, canyons, and currents been discovered on the ocean bottom, by scientists using submarines. These are exciting times for oceanographers and marine biologists. Explorations of the ocean depths, from shallow coral reefs to the deepest trenches, have yielded surprising discoveries.

No Easy Answers

Unlike other planets, the earth is blue when seen from space, because of the vast bodies of water that cover most if it. Life began in this blue mass. The saltiness of our blood matches the saltiness of the oceans, reflecting the fact that life evolved from the sea.

The oceans offer a tremendous amount of space for various types of animals and plants to thrive. As Andrew Todd Newbury points out in his book, *Life in the Sea,* there is one thousand times more space for creatures to live in the ocean than on land and in the air combined.

The sheer vastness of the oceans often makes it difficult for scientists to pinpoint the reasons for and effects of certain things that happen in the ocean. Here are a few examples:
• Monterey Bay was once the site of a huge sardine fishery, but it disappeared after World War II. Scientists still cannot prove that the

Huge schools of anchovies sometimes congregate for days along coastlines. Fishermen have long located these schools by scanning the horizon for birds that are feeding. Anchovies and sardines seem to occupy the same niche within their environment, and when one population is on the rise, the other seems to fall. Anchovies feed by flaring their shiny gill covers and filtering small particles from the water. The school appears to sparkle and flash as the fish feed.

The blue shark (top) roams the open ocean hunting for food. This type of shark has been known to attack man, but like most sharks, it's not as dangerous as most people think. The green turtle (above) is an endangered species that once flourished throughout the world. Like all marine turtles, the green turtle has a long lifespan, takes many years to mature to a point where it can reproduce, and lays its eggs in the sand where they are susceptible to predators. Consequently, green turtles are in danger of becoming extinct from fishing, nest raiding, and destruction of habitat.

sardines disappeared because there were too many fishermen harvesting them, though they suspect this was a primary cause. However, evidence also shows that the sardine population has gone up and down in the past even when there haven't been fishermen around.

• In the 1980s, coral reefs in the South Pacific were devastated by voracious herds of crown-of-thorns starfish, but whether the population explosion of these starfish was a result of man's pollution or natural cycles is still not known conclusively. Much evidence supports both possibilities.

• The impact of oil spills on wildlife is surely harmful, but scientists usually cannot provide numbers to prove this harm, since most areas have not been studied before they are damaged by a spill.

But scientists do know with certainty that despite their vastness, the oceans have proven to be astonishingly fragile habitats. In the Bahia de Los Angeles, off the inland coast of Baja, Mexico, giant squid were once abundant and arrived each spring. However, it only took one summer of intense fishing by Japanese squid boats to completely wipe out this population. The giant squid have never returned. Many large marine animals—such as turtles, sharks, dolphins, and whales—have long lifespans and take many years to mature and reproduce. A small shock to a population of these animals might drive them to extinction.

And shocks do come over and over. Gill and drift nets—which trap all types of marine life unselectively in the open ocean—may be wiping out animal populations that have scarcely been seen by man. The oceans are so vast, and so unknown, that humans often treat them unwisely, giving little thought to what effect dumping toxic wastes, plastics, nuclear wastes, and sewage into the sea will have on ocean life. While for years the government thought it was safe to dispose of nuclear waste by sinking it to the bottom of the ocean, recently researchers have discovered strong currents deep in the ocean that they think could quickly transport discarded nuclear waste back to the surface waters, contaminating coastlines and beaches.

I've been diving and photographing under water for many years—you'll read about my experiences at the beginning of each section—and am continually surprised by what the ocean has to offer. I hope that you'll share in my love of the ocean, through the photographs and words in this book. *Norbert Wu*

Spinner dolphins are fast-moving, gregarious marine mammals famed for their acrobatic jumps and leaps from the water.

THE OPEN OCEAN

The water off the California coast was like soup, a strange green vegetable broth filled with uncountable swarms of tiny crustaceans. But I was looking for something bigger—a giant shark. I strained my eyes, peering into the greenness, and cursed my mask for making the stray beams of light from the surface flicker in my sight like dancing ghosts. Suddenly, a shadow ahead gained form and substance, and I kicked toward it as fast as I could. There, close enough to touch, was the shape of a shark. The dorsal fin was as tall as me, and the huge form swept past with a sweep of its long, bladelike tail. The fish was at least twenty-five feet long. I tried to squelch all thoughts of the two kayakers who had been attacked and killed just the day before by a great white shark. But this was no man-eater. In fact, out of 441 species of shark, only six are known to have attacked humans. The type of shark I was chasing is the second largest fish in the world, the basking shark.

FLOATING PASTURES

Life underwater shares many characteristics with life on land. As on land, the food chain starts with plants, which capture the energy of the sun and use it to grow. As on land, the oceans have animals that congregate in herds, like cows, swarm in multitudes, like insects, and dart about in flocks, like birds. Unlike on land, however, most plants in the ocean are microscopic structures that float with the currents.

These plants need nutrients and minerals such as nitrogen and carbon to grow. Most areas of the ocean don't have great supplies of these nutrients. So, when sufficient nutrients are present, these tiny plants, called phytoplankton, reproduce explosively, giving rise to "plankton blooms" which turn the water green and murky. Blooms usually occur close to shore, where upwelling of deeper water and coastal runoff bring the necessary nutrients to the surface layers of the ocean, and where enough light is available to allow photosynthesis to take place. The infamous "red tides" of the Atlantic coast, where the water is actually darkened and shellfish become poisonous to eat, are caused by dinoflagellates, one-celled plants that can actually swim.

The ocean off the California coast feeds an abundance of life unrivaled in the world. The Pacific Coast is blessed with currents of cold water and life-giving coastal winds, both of which tumble down the coast, leaving nutrients in their wake. Cold waters are richer in plants and animals than warm waters, since they hold a greater amount of nutritious dissolved gases. The north-to-south winds blow the top layer of water away, causing upwelling.

Jacks and tunas are fast swimming, voracious fish of the open ocean. They travel in huge schools.

Krill (right) in Antarctica and other areas of the world's oceans provide food for the largest animals on earth, the baleen whales. Jellyfish, sharks, a variety of fish, and some birds also eat krill. Mysid shrimp (below) are found in very deep water.

Tiny Animals of the Sea

The tiny plants of the ocean support numerous small crustaceans and other animals, called zooplankton. In subzero waters in the Arctic, the water teems with animals called copepods, or *Calanus finmarchicus,* their Latin name. These tiny crustaceans are among the most important and common animals in the ocean. About the size of a grain of rice, they make up the diet of everything from humpback whales to herrings. Copepods can be found just about anywhere in the upper layers of the ocean, and so can other tiny, swarming animals. Krill, isopods, and mysid shrimp can all be found in great swarms, and provide food for whales, sharks, and smaller fish.

Grazers of the Sea

Basking sharks and whales are an example of a basic fact about the oceans: The very largest animals survive by grazing on the smallest food sources, the microscopic plants called phytoplankton, and tiny animals called zooplankton at the bottom of the food chain. The basking shark may look as big as the man-eating great white shark, but instead of killer jaws, it has a toothless mouth that it keeps open while swimming. Water sweeps into the mouth and out the gills, so that tiny animals are caught in a fine network of tissue that covers the gill openings. The largest fish in the world, the whale shark, can grow as long as

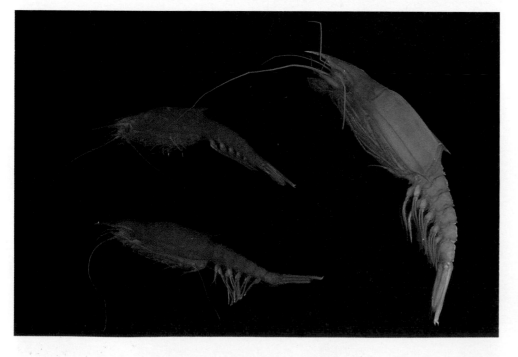

sixty feet. It swims slowly through the water with its great mouth open, grazing on plankton.

The same is true of the great whales (whales are mammals, not fish). In fact, of the large whales, only the sperm whale has teeth and eats meat. The rest are called baleen whales, because of the bristly baleen in their mouths that filters out miniscule food particles from seawater. Blue whales, the largest animals in the history of the world, are giants that grow as long as ninety-eight feet. Divers have seen these whales lunging into fantastic swarms of tiny krill, their huge mouths agape and filled with water.

The basking shark is the second largest type of fish in the world. Although it is a shark, it has no teeth. Instead, it feeds by swimming with its mouth wide open, straining plankton from the water with openings in its gills called rakers.

MOVING UP THE FOOD CHAIN

Lots of animals trap, ensnare, and filter out tiny zooplankton for food. Barnacles stand on their heads, kicking out legs like finely haired nets to filter food particles from the water. Jellyfish come in many sizes. Some are tiny spheres the size of a dime; others are monstrosities with tentacles thirty feet long. Most of them float through the water, catching zooplankton with their tentacles and drawing them up to their mouths. However, isopod zooplankton "insects" sometimes reverse the feeding cycle by hiding within a jellyfish and stealing food from the tentacles as it is brought into the gut.

Another animal, called the comb jelly, swims through the water and waves long, sticky tentacles as bait to attract larger prey. One type of comb jelly, *Beroe,* is little more than a huge mouth that can twist its body to gulp down large prey. And a creature called the pelagic salp operates like a basking shark, but on a much smaller scale. It is a strange animal about eight inches long, with an opening in each end and eight bands of muscle fibers around its body that work to bring in water which the salp filters for food. Small crustaceans called amphipods often take up residence within the salp's body, living on the food that their host brings in.

Gooseneck barnacles crowd along the surface of an abandoned fisherman's float. Any object that provides a living surface in the open ocean is quickly settled with barnacles, juvenile fish, and crabs.

Schools Spark A Feeding Frenzy

Large plankton crops along coast-lines serve as food for huge schools of anchovies and sardines, which are in turn eaten by dolphins, jacks (fast-swimming, voracious fish), sharks, sea lions, and seagulls that patrol the coast. Large schools of these anchovies and sardines turn a coastline into a frenzy of barking sea lions, diving seabirds, and fast-moving blue sharks.

Flying fish will glide along the surface of the water, picking at small marine animals with upturned mouths. Sometimes mahi-mahi chase the flying fish, making them leap from the water in long glides with the help of their winglike fins and sculling tail.

Fast-swimming tunas also travel in large schools. These fish are stream-lined models of efficiency, well-adapted for continuous high-speed cruising in the water. For example, a tuna's eye is covered by an eyelid which streamlines and protects the eye and also allows it to see more. The pectoral fins fold back into special grooves, the head is rounded and smooth, and the tail is forked to reduce friction. Ridged scales behind the gills also help the fish slip through the water at high speeds. The tuna has developed a special mode of breathing whereby it breathes by forcing water into its mouth as it moves, so it doesn't have to gulp water to get oxygen. Tunas have special muscles that help them swim without stopping.

Convict tangs often swarm over corals in

large schools.

LIFE WITHIN A JELLYFISH

In the open ocean, animals and plants live wherever they can. Large animals may host an entire community of animals that live on the outside and inside of their bodies. These animals may be parasites, which may hurt their host; symbionts, which help their host; or commensals, which have little effect on their host. A jellyfish can itself be a floating world, sheltering an entire community of crabs, medusa fish, and juvenile fish of all sorts within the protective confines of its stinging tentacles.

Many animals only seek shelter within the tentacles of a jellyfish when they are young; they later leave and seek out another home. Juvenile crabs are able to leave the safety of the jellyfish when they begin to grow tough shells and turn into heavily armored animals, protecting themselves with strong claws and camouflage coloration. Jacks spend the first part of their lives within the confines of jellyfish canopies for protection from predators. But when the jacks grow large and powerful enough to elude predators on their own, they move out and form large schools.

A juvenile triggerfish makes its home among the reproductive organs of an Aurelia, or moon jellyfish. It is protected by the jellyfish's stinging tentacles, which it is adept enough to avoid.

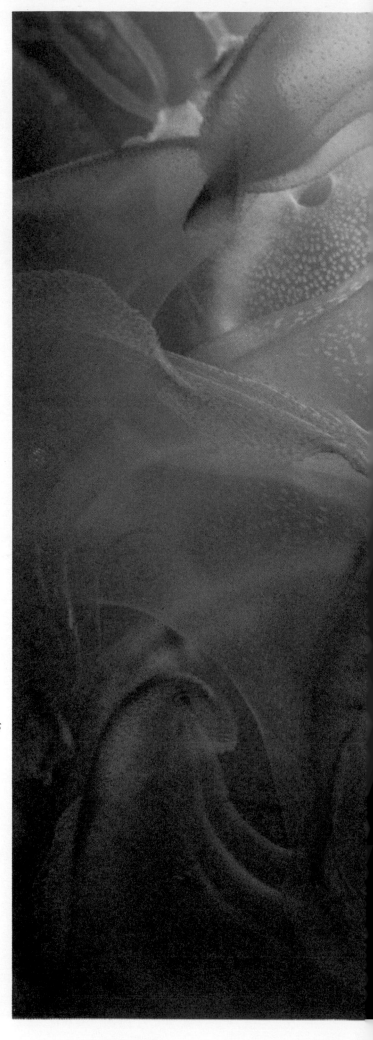

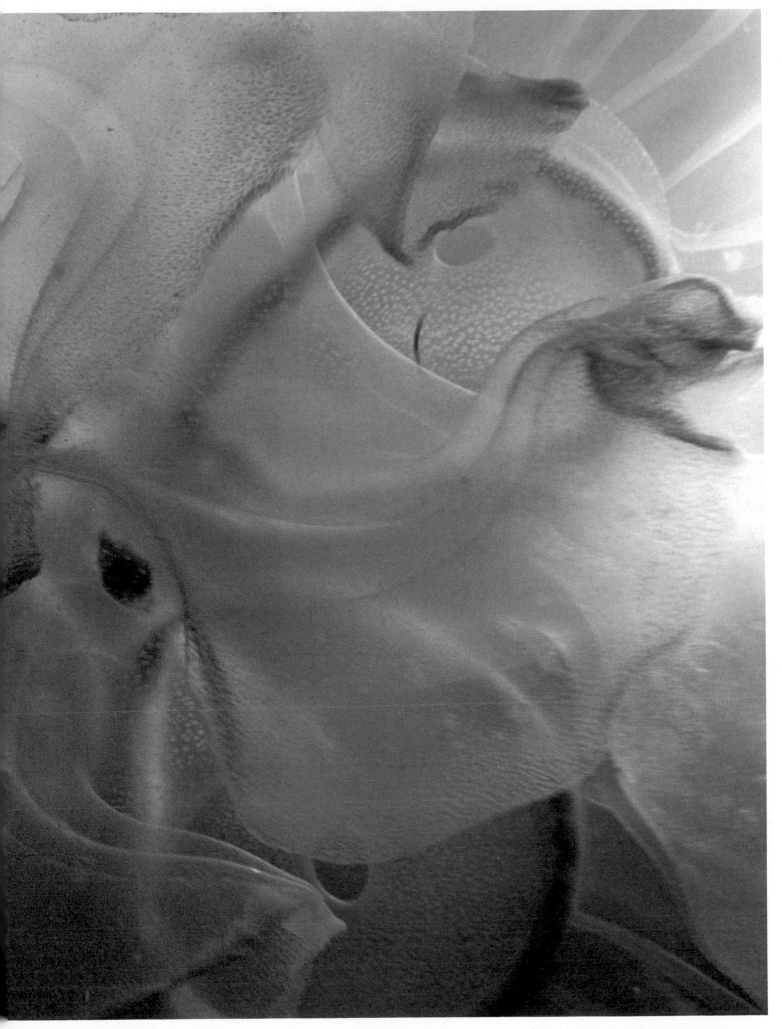

This bizarre larval slopefish, called
Exterilium larva *by scientists, is the*
only specimen of its kind ever found.
The species has not yet been identified.
The strange, trailing piece from its
stomach may serve to camouflage the
slopefish, making it look like a piece of
seaweed. This adaptation may be useful
for attracting edible small fish and
crustaceans, because it looks to them
like a safe floating shelter.

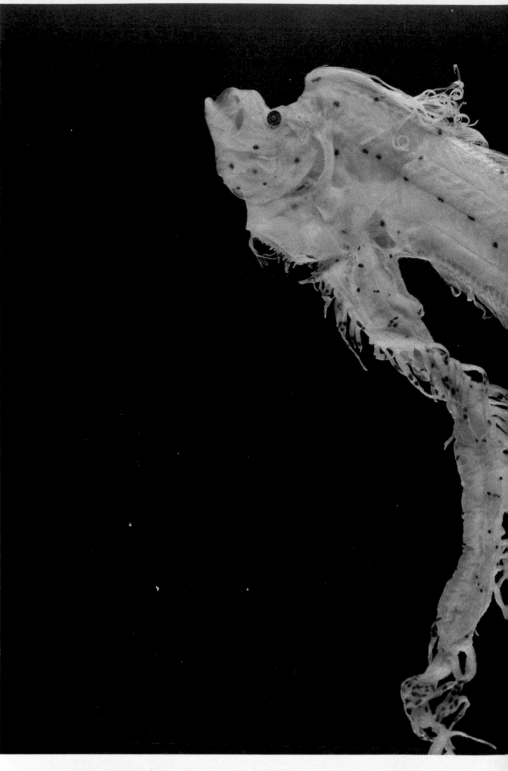

Floating Masses

Not only large animals attract animals of the ocean that are seeking shelter. Any floating mass in the open ocean may serve as a refuge for various animals. Floating masses of kelp, uprooted by winter storms and carried far offshore, have innumerable crabs, fish, and other invertebrates living, feeding, and reproducing within them. Sargassum weed, which grows in the warm, still waters of the Sargasso Sea of the North Atlantic, hosts numerous species of sargassum fish, triggerfish, and other animals, and patches are often visited by turtles, mahi-mahi, and tuna in search of prey.

The amount and diversity of life that gathers around floating objects in the open ocean is astounding. Fishermen have long used this knowledge to find groups of fish.

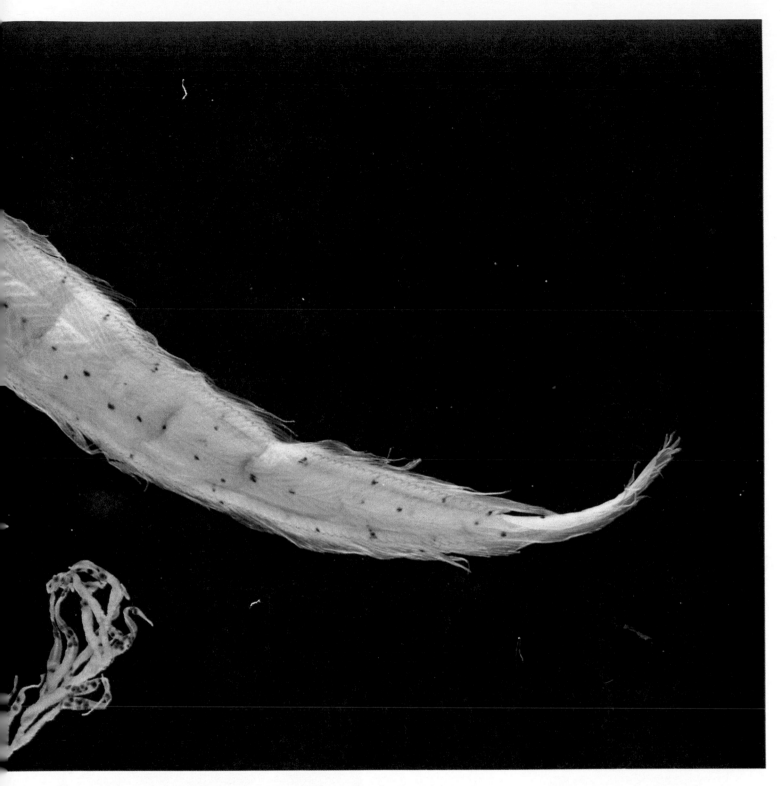

In the South Pacific, a floating log no larger than the front door of a house may have a school of 1,500 tuna underneath it. Steven Callahan, a sailor who was marooned on a small raft for seventy-six days, reports that a school of mahi-mahi, sharks, and numerous pilot fish followed his raft for days on end. Eventually, South Pacific islanders saw his raft, and though they didn't know what it was, they boated out to it because they knew there would be fish around it they could catch. Though they were surprised to find a raft carrying a starving man, they still took advantage of the good fishing around the raft.

Many governments and fishermen have created artificial fishing grounds in the open ocean by setting buoys or rafts of bamboo anchored in deep waters. Tuna, wahoo (large mackerel), mahi-mahi, and numerous game fish congregate around these buoys.

Some animals have evolved to resemble floating objects, and they also attract a variety of prey. The juvenile slopefish, found in the equatorial Pacific near New Guinea, resembles a floating mass of algae. According to some scientists, this deceptive camouflage attracts food such as crabs and fish that the slopefish eats.

UNUSUAL ANIMALS OF THE OPEN OCEAN

The open ocean is the nursery ground for innumerable interesting marine species. The young ocean sunfish looks like a tiny yellow pincushion, nothing at all like the six-foot monstrosity it becomes as an adult. The fierce-looking but gentle six-foot long wolf eel of the Pacific coast spends the first part of its life as a beautiful, transparent eel. The Moorish idol spends its adolescence as a silvery, spiny fish, floating in open ocean currents, until it finds a coral reef on which to live. When it finds a suitable reef, it loses its spines and changes into the brilliantly colored reef fish seen in Hawaii and the South Pacific.

Wolf eels such as this one can grow as long as six feet, and when they are this big they live in holes and crevices. But at the beginning of their lives, when they are small and transparent, wolf eels live in the open ocean.

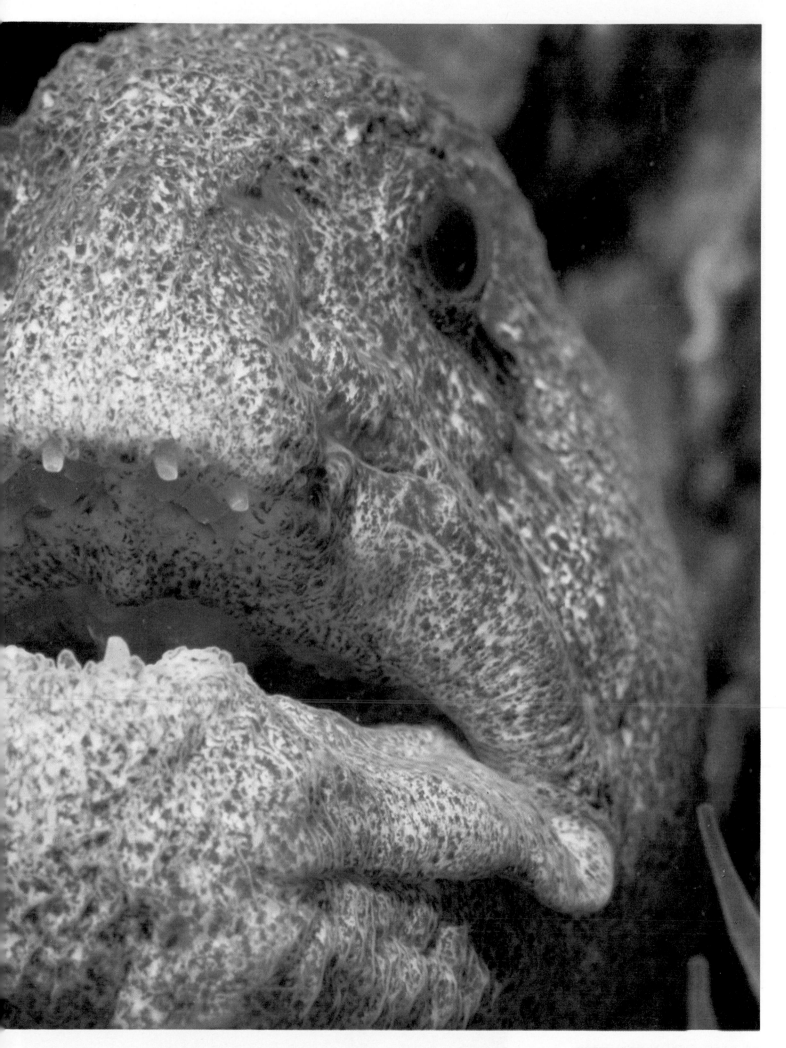

The female argonaut, or paper nautilus, (above) *is a pelagic octopod which carries a light egg case about with her. The male argonaut is only one-twentieth the size of the female. The sea butterfly* (right) *is a pelagic snail that feeds exclusively on its cousin, the shelled pteropod. It swims with large feet which have been modified into arms, and attacks with a tentacled mouth that seizes the prey and holds it.*

Paper Nautilus

The paper nautilus, also called argonaut, is a type of octopus that lives in the open ocean. The female has a delicate egg case, in which she incubates eggs. The male carries his sperm in one of his arms. When a pair mates, the female breaks off the arm, attaches it to her body, and uses it to fertilize her eggs and feed them. One female may have several male arms.

Snails

Heteropods, a type of open-ocean snail, have lost the heavy shells of their land relatives. Pteropods are another class of open-ocean snail. One class has lost its shell and looks like a butterfly (they are called "sea butterflies") with feet modified into wings. Other open-ocean snails have shells and eat by throwing out a mucus web to trap food particles. The shell-less pteropods are voracious predators. They feed exclusively on shelled pteropods, shooting tentacles out from their mouths to hold the struggling prey so it can be eaten.

Collective Animals

Siphonophores are a class of stinging animals that blur the line between group and individual. They consist of three distinct parts: a gas float at the top, swimming bracts in the middle, and stinging tentacles at the bottom. The animal is not exactly a single individual. The three parts act independently, each performing a specific function for the good of the whole. The potent, floating Portuguese man-of-war is a member of this class. Most siphonophores, however, do not float at the water's surface but instead move up and down through the water.

Another unusual animal is the larvacean, which uses its own secretions to weave a fine net that it both lives in and uses to trap food particles. The animal looks like a tadpole as it weaves its tail back and forth to circulate water and bring food within its net.

This siphonophore is made of individual parts which work together, blurring the line between individual and community. No part could survive without the others. The parts shown here include stinging cells, swimming bracts, and a gas float.

Exploring the Open Ocean

Diving in the open ocean, sometimes called blue-water diving because you can't see the bottom, only a deep shade of blue, is tricky. Space and depth are easily confused: An animal twenty yards down may appear to be nearby. Blue-water diving takes getting used to. The diver must watch his or her depth closely, as it is easy to go very deep, very quickly. Scientists diving in blue water have devised methods of dealing with the possibilities of strong currents and disorientation by using a system of safety divers and tethers.

Arctic Blue Water

When you add the problems of the arctic temperatures to blue-water diving, things get very difficult. Diving in freezing water can be dangerous. A diver's air regulator may freeze up if the diver breathes too hard. And the valves on the diver's suit may also freeze up, causing the suit to fill with air like a balloon, shooting the diver to the water's surface. This can cause air bubbles that block the flow of oxygen to the brain, which is deadly.

Scientists are beginning to do more research in the open ocean (above). Blue water diving, or diving in "bottomless" water, as this scientist is doing, is becoming more common. A scientist studies the marine life that is attracted to floating objects in the open ocean (opposite).

CORAL REEFS

There was one fish on a reef in Panama I saw every day for five months. He was one of the tiniest animals on the reef, only the size of my fingernail, and yet his large red eyes were visible from ten feet away. He made his home in an abandoned shell that was set in a massive head of brain coral. From the safety of this burrow, he darted out to catch pieces of food that floated past in the current. I visited his reef day after day while conducting a sea urchin study. After many visits, this fish became accustomed to my presence and ventured out of his hiding place to move around on my open hand. Later, I discovered that he belonged to a rare species of fish called the spotjaw blenny. Recently identified by marine biologists, this fish doesn't live anywhere else but along fifty miles of the Caribbean coast of Panama.

WHAT IS A REEF?

A reef can be made of rock, sand, coral, sunken ships—even tires and old cars. Anything that provides a stationary surface for ocean life to grow on can be a reef. Most often, reefs are made of coral or rock. You can spot reefs that are near the surface by the way surf boils and splashes around them. Some reefs are found in the middle of the ocean, and others are closer to shore. Pinnacle reefs are steep, narrow mountains that rise rapidly from the bottom to near the surface. These spires of rock can provide an oasis of life in the middle of the ocean, and huge schools of fish, sharks, and other life may be attracted to such areas.

A profusion of life lives on the edge of coral walls, nourished by food that floats in the water currents that pass by. Here a scientist examines life on a coral reef.

OCEAN CURRENTS AND REEFS

The oceans of the earth move in great, predictable currents, and the way they move determines the location of coral reefs. In the Northern Hemisphere, ocean currents sweep clockwise from the equator to the Arctic and back down to the equator. Ocean currents travel counterclockwise in the Southern Hemisphere. Ocean waters warm up as currents travel from east to west in the hot equatorial zones, and so the Indo-Pacific region, which includes the northwestern coast of Australia and the South Pacific islands, is known for warm, tropical waters and accompanying coral reefs.

The Pacific coast of California receives ocean currents coming down from the north, in a downward sweep from the Arctic. Other oceans also receive cold water from the Arctic or Antarctic oceans. This water is full of nutrients, and it supports the diverse animal communities found in the rich kelp forests off the west coasts of North America but doesn't support any coral reefs. This general rule of ocean circulation explains why coral reefs, which need warm, tropical water to live, are almost always located on the eastern side of land masses. For instance, the only coral reef of the United States is located on the east coast, off the tip of Florida.

Like the reef-building corals, these solitary stony corals (right, above) surround themselves with a limestone skeleton. A sea fan (right, below) is actually a colonial animal closely related to anemones and corals. A horny skeleton forms into fan-like shapes which face the currents, so the polyps can sift food particles from the water.

Coral

It may surprise you to know that coral is alive. The bleached, white sections of coral you see in shell shops are only piles of skeletons, as representative of living coral as the bones are representative of a colorful tropical fish. The skeletons form when animals called coral polyps secrete limestone to protect their soft bodies. Over generations, and thousands of years, colonies of these animals work together to gradually build up the huge, intricate limestone structures that exist off tropical coasts and islands. The coral reefs are the most immense structures ever built by any animal, man included.

Scientists describe three major types of coral reefs. Fringing reefs grow in shallow water, close to and along a coast. Barrier reefs are larger, farther away from a coast, and continue on for longer distances. Australia's Great Barrier Reef is the most famous example, and the barrier reef off Belize, below Mexico on the Caribbean, is the world's second largest. The third

type of reefs are called atolls. These are formed from volcanic islands that have sunk slowly enough for corals to build upon them, and they have a ring of corals surrounding a central lagoon. This depression is the crater of the volcano that originally formed the island.

Layers of Life

Coral colonies take on a great many shapes and forms. Brain corals form massive, solid boulders, while staghorn corals form elaborate branching colonies that provide shelter for a multitude of shrimp, crabs, and fish. Fire coral, called that because if you touch it, your skin will hurt like it's been burned, either covers other corals or forms plates. Soft corals, or sea fans, are closely related to stony corals, but do not form hard limestone skeletons. As corals grow together and over each other, caves and large tunnels form. Worms, oysters, and other animals burrow deep into coral heads, leaving the interior full of holes. All of these spaces provide homes for various animals.

The polyps that build these reefs are delicate and require warm, clear water to thrive. Large temperature changes, big waves, and sediment can kill them quickly. Corals catch food with stinging tentacles. They spread when their young are carried off by ocean currents to form new coral colonies. With the aid of an algae that lives in their tissues, corals produce their own food from the energy of the sun. When two organisms or animals work together like this, their relationship is called symbiosis.

Many reef animals help each other. Small, brightly colored shrimp and fish dot the surface of large sponges and brain corals. These animals serve as neighborhood barbers, cleaning the surfaces and mouths of much larger fish, such as groupers and snappers. Normally quite ready to eat shrimp and small fish, the larger fish allow the cleaners to swim all over their bodies and even within their mouths. One small fish, the saber-tooth, or false cleaner blenny, takes advantage of this mutually beneficial truce. It pretends to be a cleaner fish, and waits near a cleaning station. When an unsuspecting fish comes near, the saber-tooth blenny darts in, bites off a chunk of flesh, and then speeds away to safety.

Other animals are helped by the coral itself. At first glance, a large coral sea fan appears empty, but a closer inspection reveals that it is home to a number of animals. Spider crabs, with colors matching those of the sea fan, hide and feed' among its branches. Long-nosed hawkfish dart about along the surface of the fan, and tiny gobies blend in with the branches. Cowries, bristle starfish, fire worms, shrimp, and small fish all use the sea fan for shelter and food. Almost every available surface on the reef is colonized and used.

The large red eyes of this tiny spotjaw blenny may serve to scare off predators (above). An abandoned worm tube (left) is home to a spotjaw blenny.

Staying Alive

Every type of fish on the reef has a different way of fending off predators and getting food. During the daytime, huge schools of orange and purple fish called fairy basslets move out from the shelter of the reef, seeking to reach plankton passing in the current. At night, the basslets sleep deep within the reef, and their place on the reef edge is taken by large-eyed squirrelfish and soldierfish. During the day these shy fish can be found in large groups within the caves of the reef, waiting for darkness. Sharks, barracuda, and other fast-moving predators cruise the edge of the reef, waiting for an unwary fish to venture too far from shelter. These large predators are quick to seize an injured or slow animal.

Other predators, such as frogfish and scorpionfish, are ambush hunters. They lie in wait on the bottom, looking very much like a piece of sponge or rock. Parrotfish wander about from coral head to coral head, gnawing off chunks of coral and crushing them with their strong teeth. They feed on the worms and polyps within the coral and crush the limestone, creating sand. Butterflyfish and angelfish usually pair off as mates, and they patrol established territories, browsing on sponges, corals, and other invertebrates. Sponges grow on reef walls, drawing in water through numerous small holes on their body and filtering out food particles from the

water. Water is expelled through a large central opening. Sea fans grow in currents, where plankton is brought within reach of their numerous stinging polyps. Bristle and feather starfish often climb up to the tops of the sea fans, taking advantage of stronger currents. They wave sticky arms about in the water to catch food particles passing by. Most of these filter-feeding invertebrates do not extend their arms during the daylight, however, so butterflyfish and other fish can't bite them off.

At night, the predators of filter feeders have gone to sleep, and the reef comes alive with animals crawling out from their hiding places to spread out their arms and feed. Basket stars, which have thousands of arms, spend the day wrapped around the base of a sea fan. When night falls, they travel up to the top of a sea fan or coral head and spread out enormous, intricately branched, sticky arms to collect food. Crabs, shrimp, and small fish all come out of hiding and harvest algae and

debris under the cover of darkness. Most of the colorful fish of the day find suitable spots to spend the night. Angelfish and butterflyfish darken their bodies at night and sleep hidden in coral caves. Parrotfish also hide within coral for protection against night hunters, such as moray eels. Some parrotfish even make a mucus net which completely surrounds them. Scientists believe that this net prevents the smell of the parrotfish from attracting predators.

An azure vase sponge feeds in the waters of a coral reef (left). Sponges are primitive animals that filter water through pores on their sides. After filtering out food from the water, a sponge expels the excess water through a large opening in its center. Angelfish (top) are common on some reefs. Here, an emperor angelfish swims along a reef in Fiji. Parrotfish (opposite) feed on coral and expel sand.

REEFS IN PERIL

Reefs are constantly endangered by natural and man-made perils. The polyps that build the coral reef are tiny and delicate. They can be smothered by sand and dirt, killed by heat and cold, and destroyed by storms and waves.

Hurricanes sometimes produce huge waves that reduce reefs to rubble. However, this natural process may actually be beneficial to the reef in the long run. The rubble and coral debris from a storm-ravaged reef is cemented together by coral-line algae and other plants and animals. Eventually this process produces a strong foundation for another generation of coral polyps to settle on.

Damselfish swim in the ocean off of Baja, Mexico (pages 42 and 43). At right, symbiotic clownfish swim over a giant anemone on a reef off of Fiji.

Crown-of-thorn starfish (top) *feed on coral by turning their stomachs inside out,*

spreading them over coral, and digesting the coral tissues. At bottom is the arm of a

crown-of-thorns starfish.

What is to Blame?

Many coral reefs are in danger of dying or disappearing. Resort developments and cities built at the edge of reefs often produce a great deal of sediment that smothers the corals. Hotels that alter the shoreline may cause new currents to form. These currents may bring in sand that smothers the reef. In Australia's Great Barrier Reef, scientists are concerned about a new population explosion of crown-of-thorns starfish. These starfish feed on coral by turning their stomachs inside out, spreading them over coral, and digesting the coral tissues. Before this recent population outbreak, the crown-of-thorns starfish usually kept to deeper depths. But there are now so many that they are forced to look in shallower waters for food, and the coral reefs have been over-run by these voracious, hard-to-kill predators.

Many scientists think that humans might be to blame for this problem, because they collect the beautiful shell of the trumpet triton snail. This large snail feeds on the crown-of-thorns starfish. Scientists think that the crown-of-thorns population exploded once too many of the triton shell snails were removed from the ecosystem. However, the answer might not be so simple. Other scientists say that trumpet triton shell snails don't eat many crown-of-thorns starfish in the first place, if given a choice, and so don't have much to do with the population explosion.

Human Destruction

But even if shell collectors didn't cause the explosion of crown-of-thorns starfish, there's no doubt that man is destroying coral reefs all over the world. Coral reefs are being paved over to make room for airports on many islands. Islanders in the Caribbean are overfishing many types of fish for food, and the removal of these fish from the ecosystem often leads to an overgrowth of algae and other organisms on the corals.

In the Philippines and other parts of the world, extremely destructive methods are used to take fish for food and the aquarium fish trade. Fishermen flood the reef with bleach, which drives the fish out so they can be caught, but also kills the coral and other life. Boatloads of children are taken out to the reefs and paid to dive down with only snorkeling equipment and drag nets along the bottom that scrape the reef severely, destroying it. Entire reefs are also dynamited so that the stunned fish can be collected. Coral reefs are among the most beautiful, peaceful places on earth, but the beauty and peace is easily disrupted and sometimes destroyed.

A triton trumpet snail attacks a crown-of-thorns starfish as a diver looks on (top). The snail has almost completely consumed the starfish (above). Triton trumpet snail shells are large and are actively sought by shell collectors for their magnificent, large shell, and scientists think that the crown-of-thorns starfish populations explode and damage reefs when too many triton trumpet shells are collected.

THE KELP FOREST

I will never forget the first sea lion that swirled by my head in a flash of bubbles, startling in her speed and grace. She came by only after I had finished with my picture-taking, and she took my hand gently between her jaws and pulled me away for a delightful ride through the water off the California coast. When I took off my thick gloves, she again took my hand in her strong jaws, and with just enough pressure to hold me without causing pain, she spun me around and deposited me back onto the rock that I had been standing on. It seemed like magic.

Diving in the kelp forests is an almost otherworldly experience, for the forests grow up from depths of 100 feet to form underwater cathedrals that harbor all manner of invertebrate and larger animal life.

UNDERSEA CATHEDRALS

Kelp forests are as beautiful as any redwood forest on land, and they boast a diversity of species that rivals that of tropical rain forests. Seals and other sea creatures play out life's dramas in these mysterious forests, which are pierced by shifting rays of light.

A type of snail called a limpet, attacked by the grasping arms of a starfish, lets out a slippery white mantle that allows it to escape. Huge masses of squid mate frantically and cover the ocean bottom with their eggs. A nudibranch, a brilliantly colored sea slug, attacks and feeds on an anemone and then lays its eggs among the anemone's tentacles, thereby gaining protection for those eggs. Anemones gorge themselves on anything that they can get their tentacles on, and fight each other for living space, flinging especially long stinging tentacles at each other in slow motion.

Large forests of kelp are unusual in the ocean where the majority of plant life consists of floating microscopic plants. Kelp forests grow in waters too cold for all but the most hardy underwater explorers. However, as stated earlier, the very coldness of the water contributes to the enormous wealth of life off the California coast. Kelp forests are found off the west coasts of North and South America and the southern coasts of Australia, New Zealand, and South Africa—wherever the great ocean currents sweep cool water from the polar latitudes to the coasts.

Kelp forests, based in cold water with high nutrient levels, often harbor an abundance of life, such as this school of blue rockfish.

The Kelp Plant

The kelp forest is made up of giant kelp plants which have long stems and gas-filled bulbs that keep the plants afloat. The plants grow only in coastal areas where the ocean has a suitably hard bottom and shallow depth. Adequate light levels must also be available. The species *Macrocystic pyrifera* has been reported to grow as much as three feet a day during some parts of the growing season. When the fronds of giant kelp plants reach the surface they continue to grow horizontally, forming a canopy through which the sun's rays filter.

Animals of the Kelp Forest

The kelp plant with its many interlocking branches and leaf blades provides a home for many small animals. Tiny octopi share the crevices with small shrimp and brittle starfish. Dozens of baby fish find protection as well as food among the blades at the surface in the kelp canopy. Hundreds of snails crowd the middle part of the kelp plant, feeding on dead and rotting pieces of kelp.

And the floor below the kelp forest teems with life. Female octopi brood their eggs within caves. A mother octopus never eats during her weeks-long stay with her eggs, and she dies soon after the eggs hatch. Nudibranchs (Latin for "naked gills") move about on the rocks, feeding on hydroids and sponges, and sometimes each other.

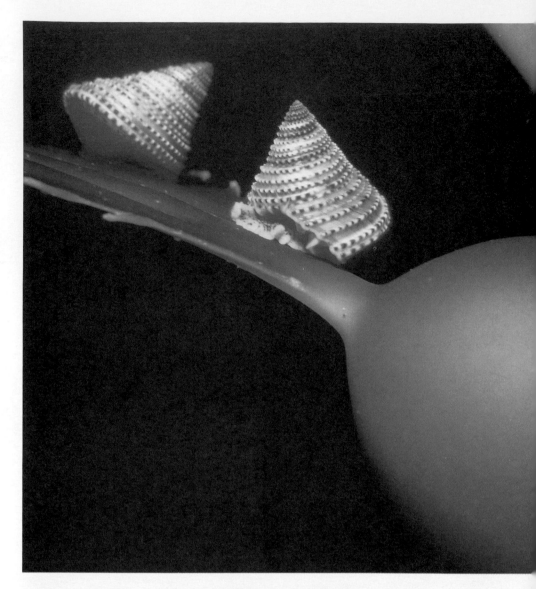

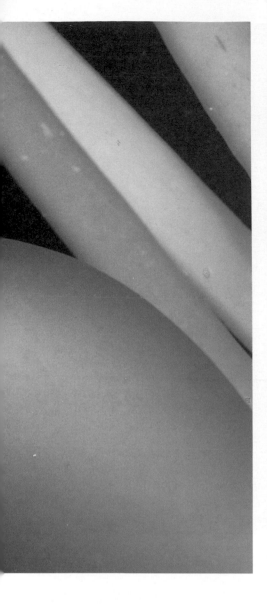

Anemones

Anemones sway slowly beneath the kelp forest, catching crabs, fish, and other animals in their tentacles. They use these stinging tentacles to paralyze their prey and bring them to their gut, which is located at the center of a ring of stinging arms. The shape of the arms indicates their preferred prey: *Metridium senile,* an anemone that situates itself on the edge of kelp beds so that currents can carry plankton to it, has delicate, fine tentacles; the fish-eating anemone, *Tealia piscivora,* has strong, stubby tentacles for grasping larger prey; the anemone *Pachycerianthes fimbratus* lives only in sandy areas and has delicate tentacles used to catch smaller prey.

The kelp forest environment supports many animals including (clockwise from opposite page, top) *jeweled-top snails on a kelp bulb; Spanish shawl nudibranch (snail without shell); and a small octopus that lives among the bases of kelp plants.*

54 THE KELP FOREST

In this sequence (clockwise from opposite page, top left) a large rainbow nudibranch feeds on a tube anemone. Upon approaching the anemone, it rears back and literally jumps into the anemone's mouth. The anemone withdraws into its protective tube, pulling the nudibranch even farther in, and the nudibranch leisurely feeds upon the stinging body. Finally, the nudibranch lays a mass of eggs within the anemone. The eggs are protected from predators by the stinging tentacles of the anemone.

Sea Slugs

Nudibranchs are among the most colorful of the kelp forest inhabitants. They are shell-less snails (sea slugs) that have brightly colored gills on their backs. They range in size from tiny animals to foot-long individuals.

One nudibranch uses anemones as a living food supply. It approaches an anemone and rears back and jumps into the anemone's mouth. The anemone then retreats into its protective tube, pulling the nudibranch even farther in. Once inside, the nudibranch feeds leisurely upon the anemone's tentacles, and the anemone has no way to get rid of it. The nudibranch sometimes even stores the anemone's undischarged tentacles within its own body and uses them for its own defense.

Escape from a Starfish

Starfish are voracious predators that feed upon almost anything that can't move fast enough to escape their grasping tube feet. In the photographs, a starfish, *Pisaster giganteus*, approaches and grasps the shell of a limpet (snail). The limpet then exudes its protective mantle and moves away to safety, its two antennae protruding.

FRAGILE WEBS OF LIFE

Kelp forests change with the seasons. The forests grow lush and thick in the summer, when sunlight and calm seas allow the plants to grow quickly and form dense canopies at the surface. In the winter, storm-driven waves batter the top of the forest, ripping away the canopies and creating sparse cover. The kelp plants linger on, however, and they give rise to new canopies in the spring and summer, completing the cycle. Very strong storms sometimes rip entire plants away from the bottom. It then takes much longer for the forest to grow back, as new plants must settle on the bottom, find a suitable surface on which to anchor, and grow quickly—without being eaten by snails, smothered by sand, or crowded out by the algae that covers the bottom rocks.

A diver descends beneath the kelp forest canopy. Large forests of kelp grow out of the ocean floor, reaching for the sunlight at the surface. These forests are unusual in the ocean, where most plant life consists of floating microscopic plants.

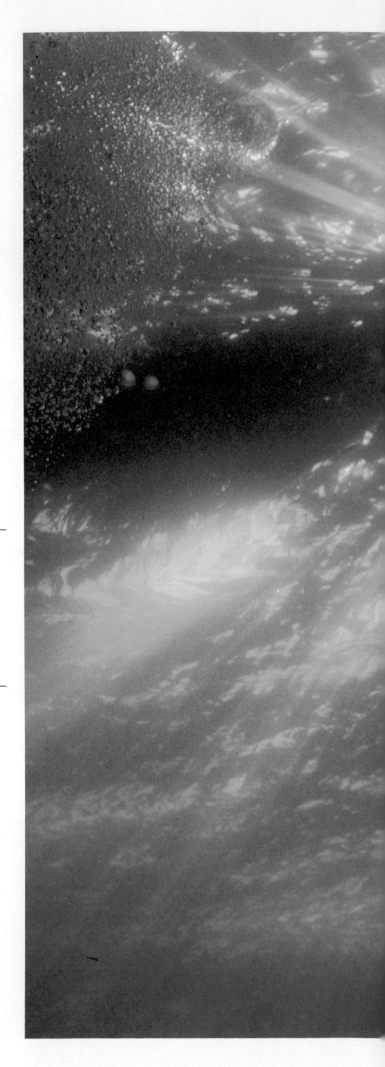

Urchin Barrens

Normally, this cycle of growth and destruction is kept in fine balance, and a healthy kelp forest will survive in an area for hundreds of years, with individual plants replacing one another constantly. This balance, however, has been destroyed in some areas off the California coast, where entire acres of once lush forest have been scraped bare by an explosive, hungry population of sea urchins. These urchins crawl across the bottom in search of algae to eat. Urchins usually feed on dead "drift kelp" and small algae cover, which they scrape off rocks, but when their population gets out of control, the urchins eat away at the base of the kelp plants. The result is an ocean bottom covered with thousands of hungry sea urchins, as well as the loss of the once lush kelp canopy and the animals that lived there.

These bare areas, called "urchin barrens," may contribute to a snowball effect: Not enough kelp is left to lessen the force of ocean waves, and so any remaining kelp may be ripped off the ocean bottom by these more forceful waves. The uprooted kelp plant is carried away with the currents, and it may uproot more plants as it becomes entangled with them.

Sea Otters Help Kelp

As in all ocean environments, the community of the kelp forest is closely connected in a fragile web, and damage to one link in this web may lead to disastrous effects for the health of the entire community. Sea otters were once abundant along the Pacific coast of North America, but they were hunted to near-extinction in the 1800s. Now they are found only along a short distance of the central California coast and along the coast of Alaska.

The sea otter is an active, voracious eater of abalone, crabs, sea urchins, and many other animals. Fishermen complain that sea otters eat too much abalone and fish. However, scientific research has uncovered evidence indicating that the presence of sea otters actually contributes to healthier and larger fish populations within the kelp forest! The sea otter's favorite foods, sea urchins and abalone, feed on kelp, and the sea otter controls these populations, thereby creating larger, healthier kelp beds.

And sea otters love a good kelp bed. Sea otters wrap themselves in kelp every night, before going to sleep. The kelp anchors them in place, and passing swells may rock a mother and pup like a cradle—the caress of the sea. Like all ecosystems on earth, the kelp forest is a fragile, interconnected community. It makes sense to pay close attention to the health of the underwater cathedrals off our coasts.

Sea otters in a kelp forest canopy (above). *Sea urchins within an urchin barrens* (opposite).

Fish Faces of the Kelp Forest

Here are some interesting portraits of kelp forest fish:

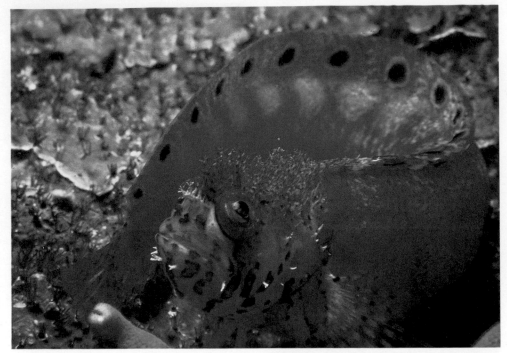

Garabaldis are brightly colored fish that guard their own piece of rock, and breed and live there. Egg nest sites may be thousands of years old—the same site is used over and over again. In the spring and summer, each male makes a nest of red algae. As a female makes her way through the kelp forest, a male will pop up from his nest and try to attract her to his nest site. If she is convinced, she will lay a batch of eggs in his nest, which he will fertilize. The male aggressively defends this nest from all intruders and vigorously cleans the nest of any dirt, urchins, or starfish that might move onto the nest.

The **mosshead warbonnet,** aptly named for its mossy head, blends in well with its surroundings.

Wolf eels are large fish that can grow to a length of six feet. They mate for life and can be found around the hole or crevice that serves as their shelter. The wolf eel's teeth are large and strong, adapted to crunching a diet of clams, sea urchins, and crustaceans.

The **convict fish** lives within California hydrocoral as part of a small community containing crabs, snails, and other animals.

Rockfish establish themselves within three-foot long borders along small boulders. They very aggressively protect their individual territories.

The **torpedo ray** uses special organs that are arranged in series under the upper part of its body to generate an electric voltage of 100-150 volts. This ray is particularly combative at night and will enfold small fish in its wings and shock them to death. Humans have even been shocked by these animals.

Lingcod are at the top of the fish food chain. They usually lie motionless, blending in with their surroundings in an attempt to ambush their prey. They are plagued by small parasites which race along their body in waves.

THE DEEP OCEAN

With the clang of the submersible's hatch, I settled down for a long ride. There was little room to turn or move about in the small steel tube that was to take me to the bottom of the ocean. As the one passenger in the small submersible, I spent my time flat on my stomach, looking through four thick windows into the dark depths. The humidity was so high in the submersible that the windows were dripping. I heard the whir of the fans and hoped that the carbon dioxide scrubber was keeping the air clean. With a swirling of water and a splash, I began my long, dark journey to the bottom of the ocean.

A trip to the bottom of the ocean can take longer than an airplane ride across America. The steel tube I was in creaked and complained for over an hour as I

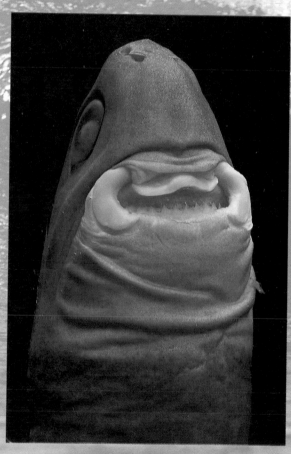

dropped down deeper and deeper. Looking outside, I watched as the steep coral
wall became darker and darker, until
finally it gave way to exposed rock. At five
hundred feet deep, the undersea landscape was covered in its eternal deep blue
twilight. At this depth, not enough light is
available to support the profuse covering
of life that is found in surface waters. But
I saw a green turtle suddenly shoot up
from a crevice in the wall, as surprised
to see me as I was to see it.

Descending deeper and deeper into
the darkness, the craft finally touched
down on a sandy bottom at one thousand
feet deep. Feather stars, ancient, primitive
relatives of starfish, were everywhere, sift-
ing the water with their arms for floating
food. In the lights of the sub, I saw shim-
mering, dancing schools of squid and
small flashlight fish in the distance. Both
the squid and the flashlight fish can generate their own *bioluminescent* light.
Strange animals live at this depth, animals
that never see sunlight, grotesque relatives
of the fish up above. It was an utterly alien
landscape for me.

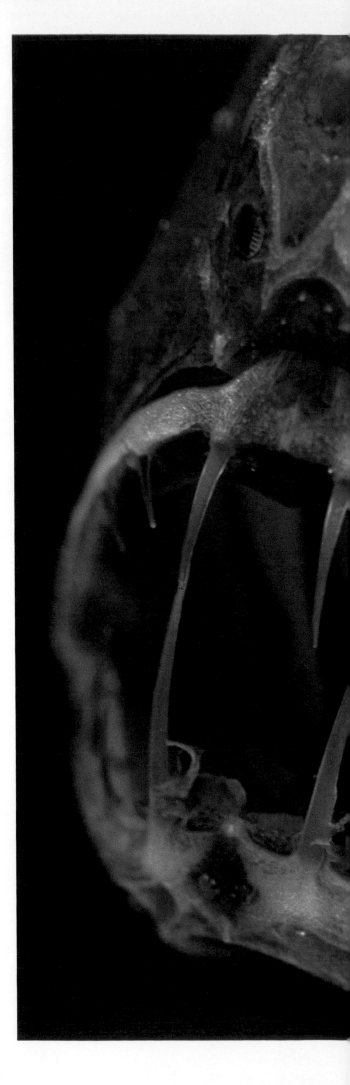

The deep-sea fangtooth has a bony, hard body and tremendous fangs.

THE VAST DEPTHS

We live on a thin skin of land covering less than one-third of our planet, bathed by sunlight. Life in the upper 300 feet of the ocean is also blessed with life-giving sunlight, and we are all familiar with the richness and diversity of life off our coasts. But all of our land and ocean surface is only the paper-thin skin of a very large onion. As mentioned before, the ocean is a vast basin averaging two and one-half miles in depth. The top, biologically productive layer represents only 2.5 percent of the ocean's capacity. Humans have only recently developed the robots and submersibles that let scientists see the other 98.5 percent, and make important discoveries. Continents have been shown to drift across our planet's surface like ice cubes in a thick milkshake. Undersea canyons rivaling the Grand Canyon in size and depth have been discovered close to coastlines. Deep sea currents as strong and swift as any in shallow waters have been found everywhere, and many new species of animals have been observed.

The deep sea swallower (right) is named for its huge, hinged mouth that opens wide to swallow prey. These fish are extremely rare and are usually found only below 5,000 feet deep. It is thought that the fish uses the light organ at the end of its tail to attract food.

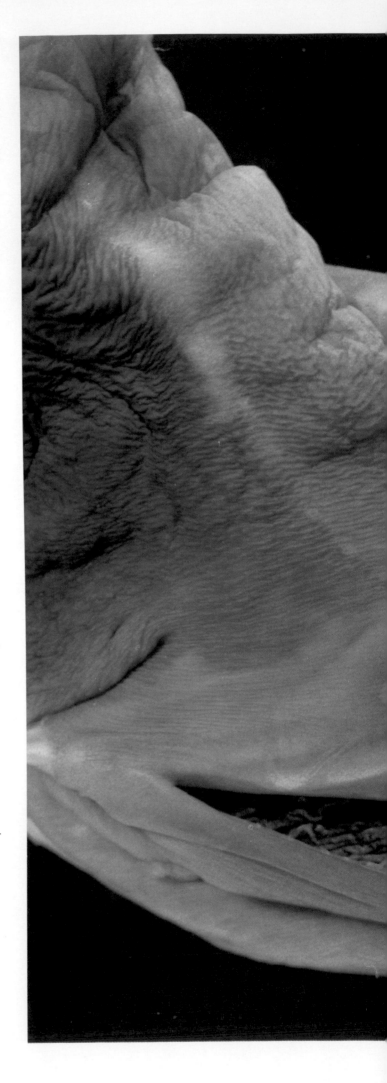

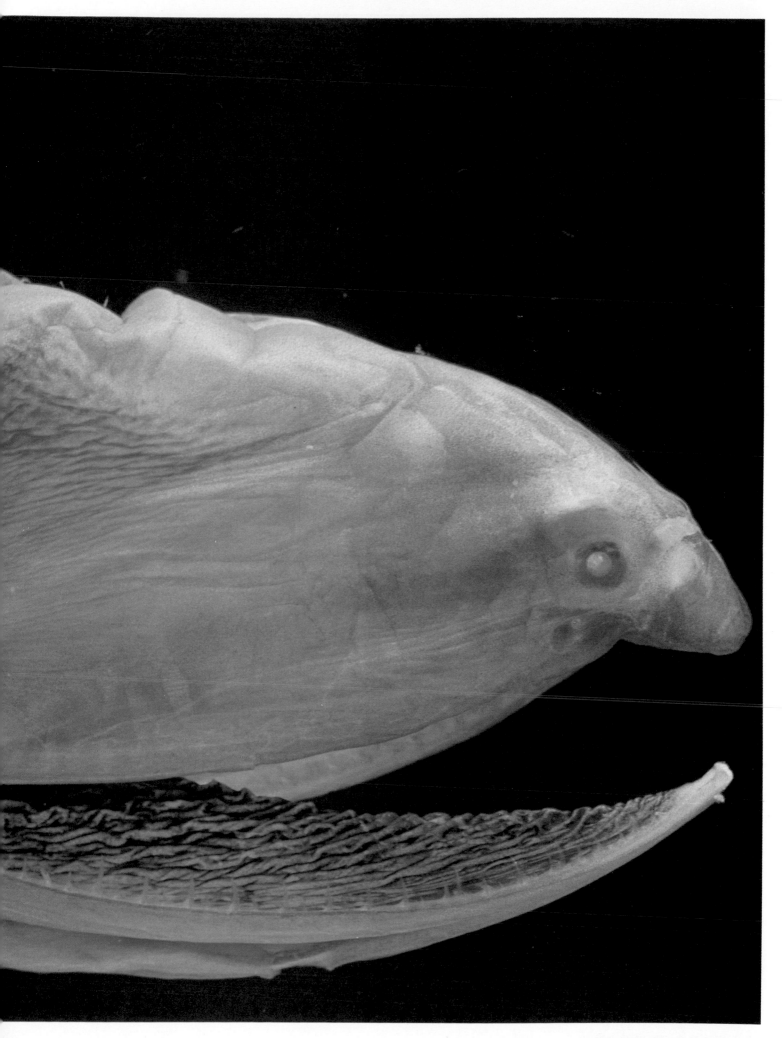

The black dragonfish is a long, thin fish that uses luminous organs along its body and in front of its mouth to attract prey. Though it looks primitive, scientists consider the black dragonfish to be an advanced species.

A Cold, Black Place

At 300 feet down, the deepest scuba divers can go, there is barely enough sunlight for a plant to produce food from the energy of light (a process called photosynthesis). Water selectively filters out red light, so that only blue-green light is present. At 3,000 feet, light from the sun is almost completely gone. At such great, dark depths, the water temperatures are generally a constant, low 39 degrees F. The pressure caused by the weight of tons of water is tremendous. Living things in the deep sea have evolved many unusual features to deal with the darkness, the scarcity of food, and the high pressures of the abyss.

The Twilight Zone

Very faint levels of light may filter down to depths of 3,000 feet, and fish in this twilight zone have developed many structures to help them survive. Many animals have large, sensitive eyes, and these fish can see thirty times better in dim light than can humans. Tubular eyes allow them to judge distance and detect prey that are silhouetted against the light coming from the surface.

To avoid casting a shadow, the prey of such fish try to blend into the background. Fish merge into light from above by being transparent, by reflecting light to match the background, or by having a very low reflective surface. Larvae of deepwater fish are often transparent. Dark colors conceal well, and red colors work just as well in the depths, where all red light has been filtered out by the water. Many shrimp as well as an entire family of fish, the whalefish, are colored a brilliant red. Some fish even generate their own light, which matches the light coming from above, so they seem invisible because they do not cast a shadow. The hatchetfish possesses light organs all along the sides of its body; these emit blue-green light at the exact intensity of the light coming from the surface.

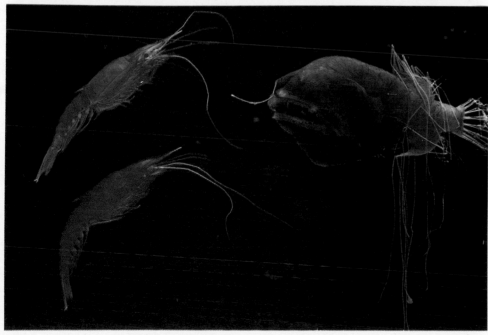

Most fish in the deep sea lay large, yolky eggs rather than huge masses of millions of tiny eggs, as most fish nearer the surface do. An example is this deep-sea anglerfish embryo (top). Deep-sea anglerfish (bottom) lure prey with a bioluminescent lure. The light is manufactured within the fish's body.

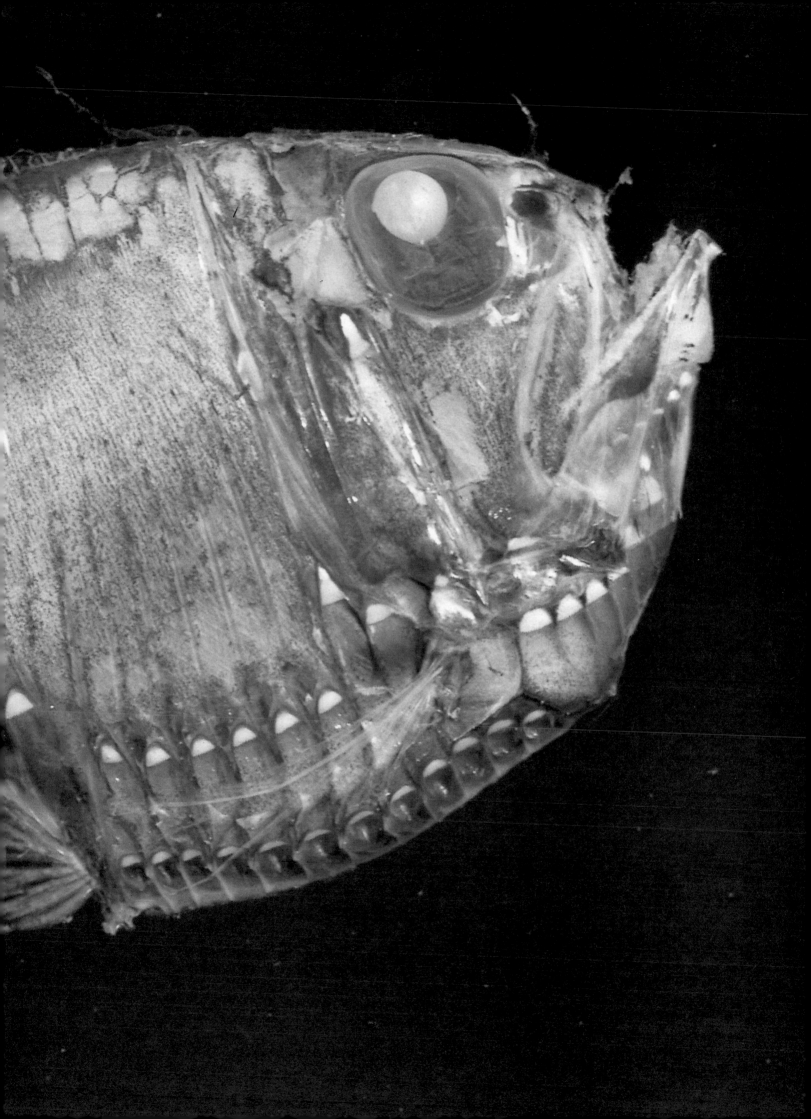

The Allure of Light

In the pitch darkness of water 3,000 feet deep, fish with fancy light sources are common, and the patterns and probable functions of these light sources are a lesson in evolution. These light sources may attract food and mates, and confuse predators. A fish may be able to identify its mate by the pattern of light organs it has. The black dragonfish can pull a black screen down to hide the light organ below its eye, and it also has a row of light cells all along its body. This fish's ability to flash these lights gives it a unique identity.

Attracting a mate with powerful displays of light is not the only function of these light organs. The female deep-sea anglerfish wriggles luminous lures to attract food; the black dragonfish has luminous barbels at the tip of its mouth, which it waves about; and the viperfish uses light organs within its mouth to lure prey right into its waiting stomach.

In an interesting turn, the *Pachystomias,* a black dragonfish, emits red light from a light organ under its eye. Since most fish in very deep waters cannot see red light, *Pachystomias* is able to use this light as a sniperscope, secretly sighting and moving in on potential prey.

Living Light

In the 1970s, scientists diving at *HydroLab,* the United States' undersea habitat in the Virgin Islands of the Caribbean, were surprised to see a constellation of flickering, moving lights off the coral wall near the habitat. The lights were only noticeable on very dark nights, and they turned

out to belong to a completely new family of fish called the lanterneye fish, named for a light-emitting organ beneath each eye. After hiding in caves and great depths during the day, these fish came up to shallower water on dark nights to feed on plankton. The light organ underneath each eye is filled with luminous bacteria, and these fish have developed special ways to turn the lights on and off at will. One type, *Kryptophanaron,* shuts off its light by pulling a dark piece of skin over the light organ. Other types, *Anomalops* and *Photoblepharon,* have their light organs, mounted on stalks, which fit into a socket, and can be turned to block out the light.

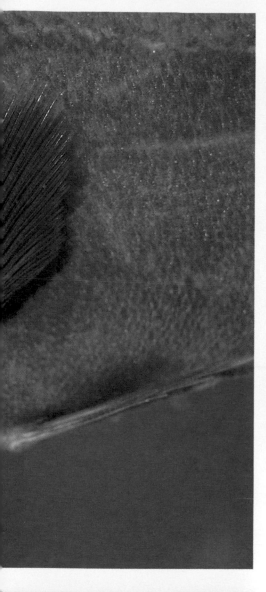

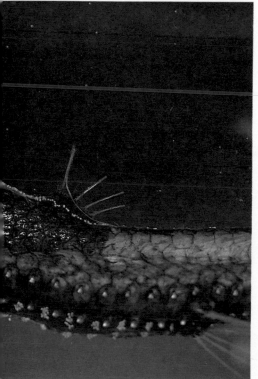

Light organs along the side of the deep-sea hatchetfish (pages 72 and 73) match the intensity and color of the water, rendering the hatchetfish nearly invisible. Its tubular eyes let it see even in the dim light of the deep sea. Here (clockwise, from opposite page, top) the flashlight, or lanterneye fish, which flashes a light organ to attract mates and prey; a deep-sea anglerfish; and a viperfish.

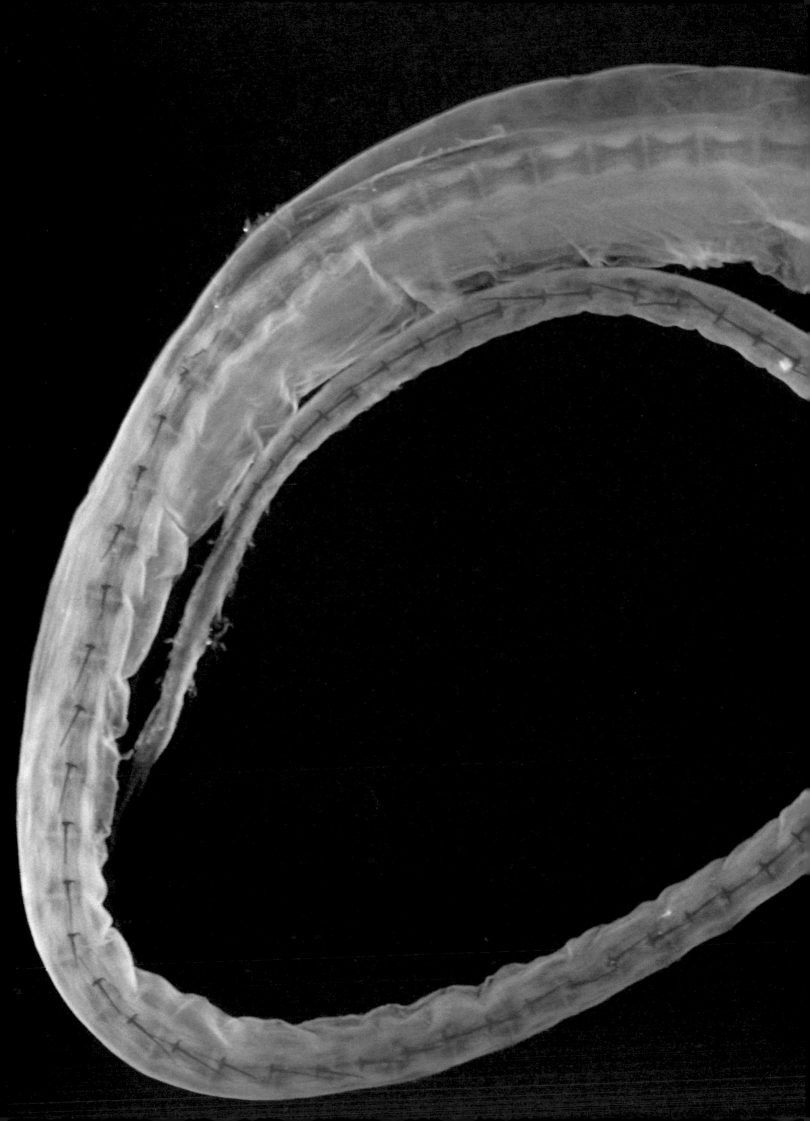

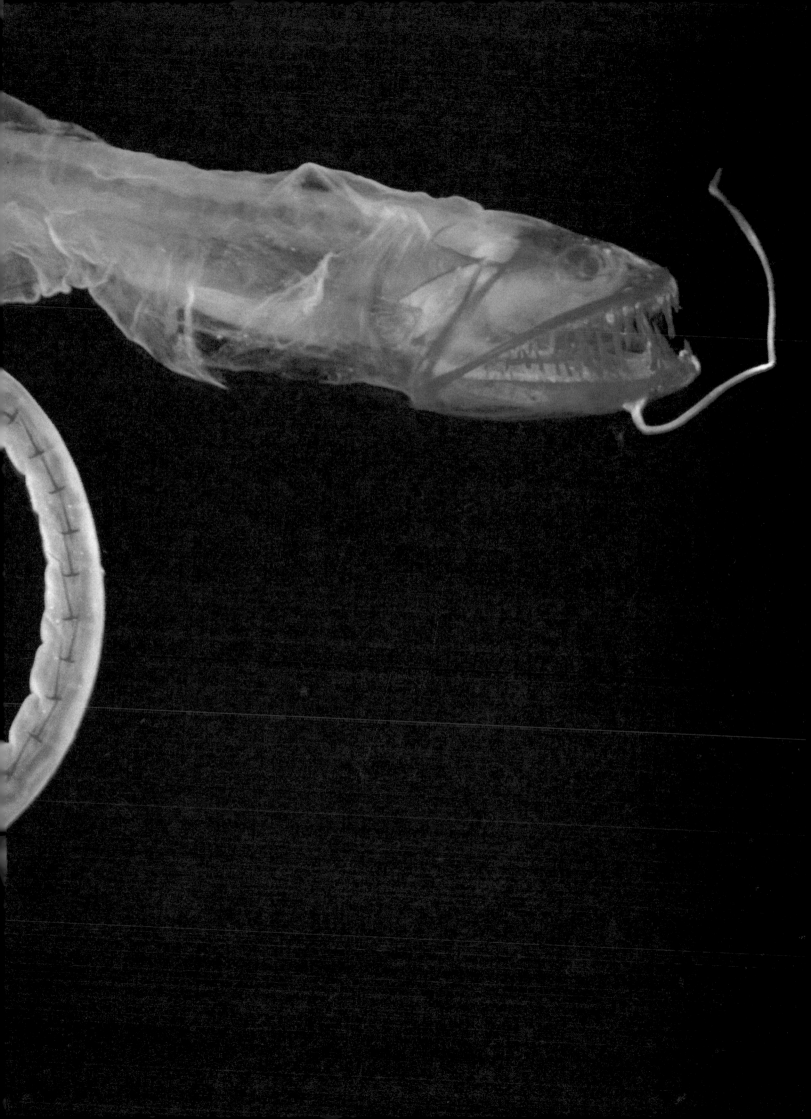

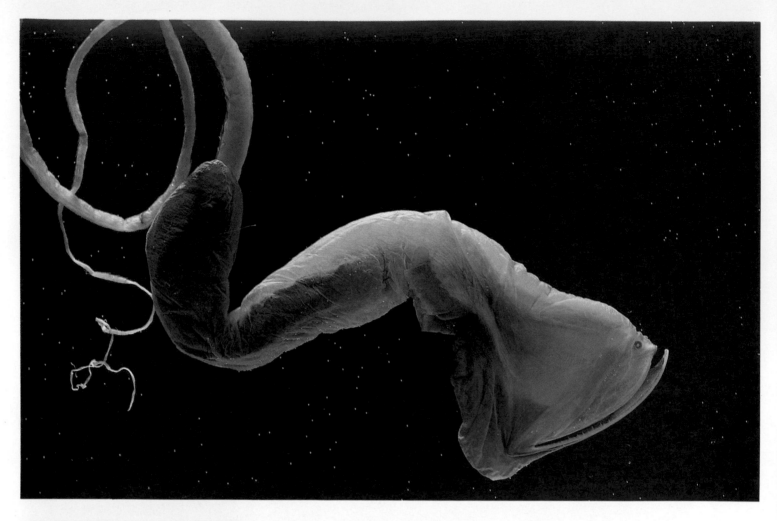

Making the Most of a Meal

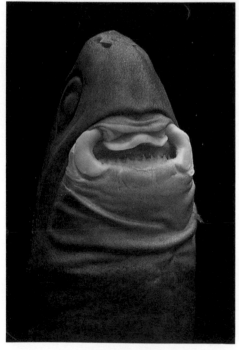

A black dragonfish (page 76) has been stained to reveal the bones.

Life in the deep ocean depends on the richness of surface waters for food. The sunken bodies of large animals such as whales may provide a rare feast for scavenging fish, which can gather to a corpse in astonishing speed. Robot cameras and manned submarines have discovered frenzied schools of hagfish (eel-like, primitive fish that burrow into a fish and eat it from the inside out), isopods (large crustaceans resembling a pillbug), and even large, six-gill sharks gathered to eat bait that's been put out thousands of meters down. Food is scarce in the deep sea. Should a fish encounter a potential meal, it will likely eat it, regardless of the size. Large female anglerfish regularly take prey two or three times their own length, and black swallowers are so named for their enormously expandable stomach, which is often found filled with large prey, nearly equal in size to the hunter.

Many fish have developed long fangs and hinged mouths to catch large prey. One type of anglerfish even has teeth in the back of its throat to keep its prey from escaping as it is being swallowed. The deep-sea swallower, *Saccopharnyx,* is a serpentlike fish with an enormous head and hinged mouth that can open like a garbage truck to swallow prey. The cookie cutter shark has jaws lined with razor-sharp teeth, and many dolphins, whales, and large fish have semicircular scars from encounters with these foot-long fish, which bite into their prey and twist away with a chunk of flesh.

The fish down in these depths don't get to eat very often, so they take full advantage of every opportunity.

Finding a Mate

It is difficult for any creature in these dark depths to find a suitable mate. How such isolated creatures find each other in the vast reaches of the ocean remains one of the great unsolved mysteries of deep-sea biology. For instance, anglerfish are extremely rare, although they are found in every ocean. Scientists report catching an average of only one anglerfish in two weeks of trawling, and one estimate is that there are fifteen or more males for every female. These males are much smaller than the females, and they have only one goal in life—to find and fertilize a female. The anglerfish has developed a strategy to guarantee that any meeting between sexes is fruitful. When a male encounters a female of the same species, he will attach himself to her with his mouth. Gradually, the male becomes a parasite of the female; his mouth fuses to her body, and blood vessels actually form between the couple. The male becomes little more than an attached sperm sac, about one-twentieth the size of the female. Sometimes several males are found attached to a single female, lifetime partners all.

Here (clockwise, from opposite page, top) is a deep-sea swallower; a deep-sea anglerfish; and a cookie cutter shark, its jaws lined with razor-sharp teeth suitable for tearing chunks of flesh from living whales, dolphins, and large fish.

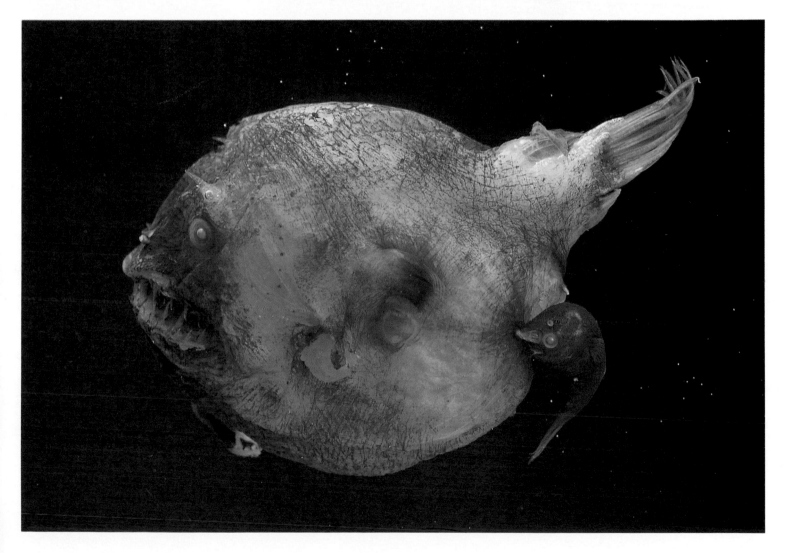

A trio of marine hatchetfish (above);

a fangtooth (below); *and a deep-sea*

anglerfish (opposite).

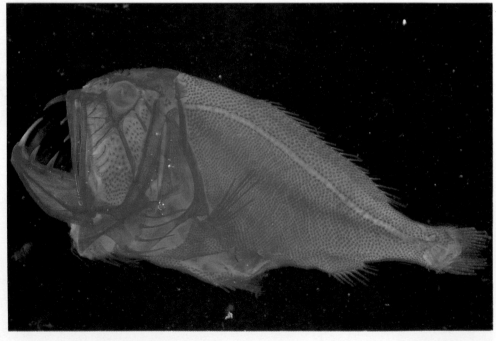

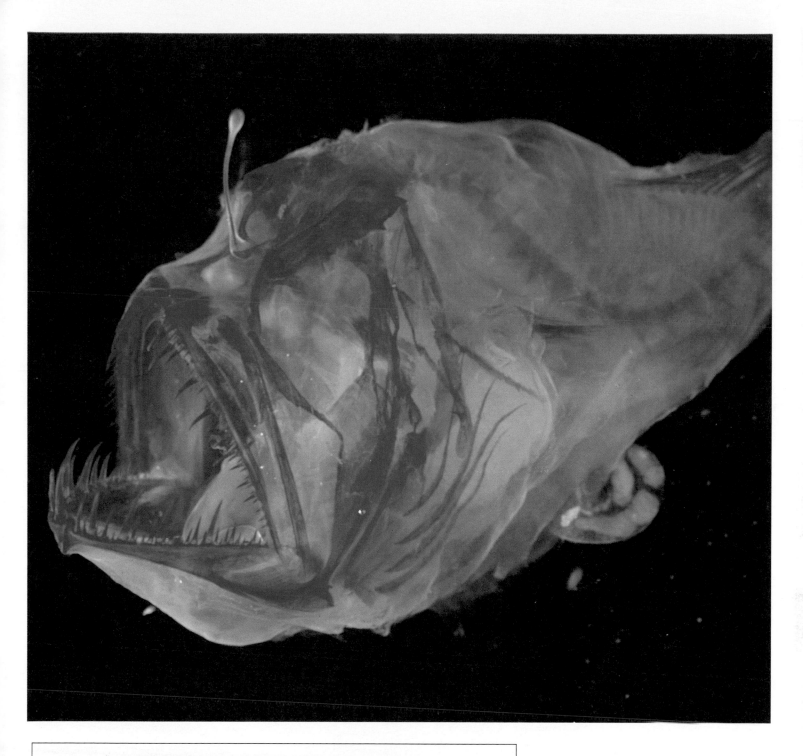

ABOUT THE PHOTOGRAPHS

*None of the specimens photo-
graphed here are more than a foot
long. They do look like monsters,
but fortunately they are very small
monsters, hardly able to threaten a
photographer in a submersible
exploring the ocean depths. To
make the photographs more useful
and interesting, the specimens in
these photographs were put through
acids and dyes that show the inter-
nal structure of the fish. Bones are*
stained red and cartilage blue.

*The bizarre deep-sea fish in these
photos were once thought to be
extremely primitive. However, scientists now know that most animals of
the deep-sea are highly advanced,
and that the various species evolved
in upper surface waters before head-
ing to the deep. One indication of
this is the amount of bone structure
(red dye) in these fish, which is a fea-
ture of more advanced fish.*

THE FUTURE

I saw her once again, or perhaps the sea lion was the sister of the one who had once played with me in the kelp forest. But her eyes were not shiny any more. She was close to death. She barely moved as I approached. The sea lion had a gill net wrapped around her neck, and the cords of the net were slowly and surely choking her to death. As I came close, she jerked up with a start and disappeared into the water, eliminating any chance of being saved. The animals that are injured in this way become shy and afraid of man, and they flee from people who, ironically, are their last hope. Almost all of them die alone, off in the open ocean, and only a few of them wash onto shore. The ocean hides its tragedies and deaths beneath a surface of waves. We see few of the effects that our nets, plastics, oils, and pollution

have on the inhabitants of the sea.

Remember the sea otter and pup, wrapping themselves in kelp for a good night's sleep? In Alaska, the Valdez oil spill soaked through the fur of sea otters just like them, robbing them of their lives. Without the insulation afforded by the air bubbles in their fur, they died. A pup cried throughout the night, in a high, bleating wail. A mother frantically licked her and her pup's body, trying to get the thick, black oil off, but to no avail. The pup died before morning, and the weak, sick mother was picked up by a team of marine mammal rescuers. They were too late. The otter's stomach was clogged with oil, and she died of exhaustion a few cold hours later. Thousands of birds, fish, and all manner of marine life died that night and the long nights after, killed by the silent spread of oil leaking from a ship that carried millions of gallons. Oil spills are a common hazard to the oceans. But they aren't the only danger the oceans face.

An oil spill is almost impossible to clean up before tremendous damage is done. The thick, gluey oil coats birds, sea otters, fish, and all manner of marine life. The long-term effects of an oil spill will last many years after the oil has been cleaned up or washed away. Oil settles to the bottom, where it may disrupt the life cycles of plankton, thus upsetting the vital first link in the food chain.

MAN'S INFLUENCE

Life in the ocean seems boundless, and it is sometimes difficult to notice where man has made an impact. However, several areas and species are threatened, most noticably those animals at the top of the food chain. Several species of great whales, seals, and even sharks are potentially endangered.

Gill nets and drift nets, which are used in the open ocean, are among the most dangerous threats to marine life yet created, with the potential of completely wiping out much life in the open ocean. Yet they are an almost invisible threat. Most people never see a gill net, and they certainly do not see the open-ocean driftnets used thousands of miles offshore. These floating nets extend for miles, capturing and drowning everything that comes their way, edible or not, rare or not, be it shark, fish, dolphin, whale, turtle, or seal. Drift nets kill all kinds of marine animals, whether or not they are useful for food. In the middle of the Pacific Ocean, more than enough drift net is laid out every night to stretch all the way around the earth at the equator— 30,000 to 40,000 miles a night. This method of fishing is incredibly wasteful.

For ocean creatures, gill nets and their open-ocean counterparts, drift nets, are invisible, indiscriminate killers. Over 45,000 miles of drift net are put out every night in the oceans of the earth. Since the nets don't pick and choose which animals they trap, many animals that are never used for food, such as these sharks, die.

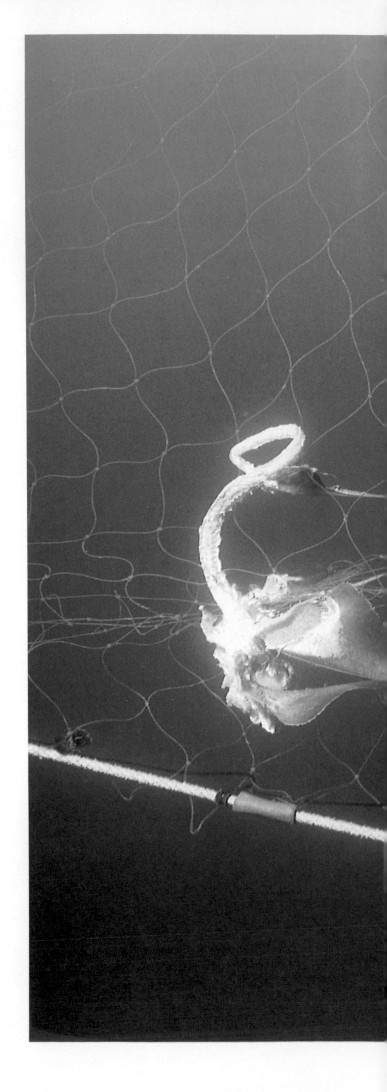

What Goes Down, Comes Up

Unlike on land, man's heavy hand in the ocean is rarely seen. Shipwrecks quickly become overgrown with algae and invertebrate life. Waste dumped far out at sea disappears into the depths—at least most people think it disappears. But this is an illusion. The waste that is dumped far out at sea sometimes reappears on beaches. Plastic bags return to the surface to entangle and sicken animals that eat them. Nuclear waste dumped far out into the great depths comes back in the form of radioactive fish. The containers holding these dangerous wastes can't be built to withstand the high pressures of the deep sea forever, and deep-sea currents carry the wastes far and wide.

This shipwreck off Grand Cayman shows how the ocean tries to take care of debris that sinks to the bottom. Algae and coral are gradually taking it over. But not all human refuse is this harmless.

Each gorgonian sea fan (above) *is actually a colony of animals that forms wiry, springy skeletons to create large "bushes" or "fans." At right is an example of the marshland that is vital to the health of the oceans. Whether or not humans should develop these marshlands is a controversial issue. Kelp bulbs* (opposite, top) *serve to keep the parts of the kelp that photosynthesize energy from the sun near the top of the water, where the light reaches them. The small red night shrimp* (opposite, bottom) *only comes out at night. Its large black eyes help it see even in the dim moonlight that reaches underwater.*

Balancing Human Needs

Our growing population is crowding the coastlines and creating a demand for more land. In this way, the marshes, wetlands, and bays along our coasts are being filled in and developed into new condominiums, resorts, and golf courses. It is precisely these areas, however, that serve as nurseries for juvenile fish, birds, and all types of marine life.

As these areas disappear, so will the early links in the marine food chain disappear. We have seen how fragile coral reefs and kelp forests can be. Resorts and cities along the edge of a coral reef can kill it quickly by changing currents and temperature, and contaminating the water with sewage and too much sand. A kelp forest can be disturbed by the tem-

perature rise or sediment from the heated waters of a power plant.

The oceans are vast, but they are fragile. Our stake in protecting the oceans and their inhabitants is high. From sea fans, sponges, and kelp, we are finding new medicines, foods, and other products. The energy of waves and tides is being harnessed to produce energy to warm our homes. Mussels, shrimp, abalone, lobsters, and many types of fish are raised in farms around the world to provide food for our tables. Seawater is routinely made suitable for drinking by desalination plants in desert and tropical areas, where fresh water is rare. It's up to us to protect our resources, and plan for the future.

METRIC CONVERSIONS

U.S. Units	Metric Equivalents
LINEAR MEASURE	
1 inch	2.54 centimeters
1 foot	0.3048 meters
1 yard	0.9144 meters
1 rod	5.0292 meters
1 mile	1,609.3 meters
1 furlong	201.168 meters
1 league	4.828 kilometers
AREA MEASURE	
1 square inch	6.4516 square centimeters
1 square foot	929.03 square centimeters
1 square yard	0.836 square meters
1 square rod	25.293 square meters
1 acre	0.405 hectares
1 square mile	2.5899 square kilometers
CUBIC MEASURE	
1 cubic inch	16.387 cubic centimeters
1 cubic foot	28.316 cubic centimeters
1 cubic yard	0.765 cubic meters
WEIGHT	
1 ounce	28.350 grams
1 pound	453.592 grams
100 pounds	45.3592 kilograms
1 ton	0.90718 metric tons

Temperature Conversions

°F	°C	°F	°C
32	0	125	51.7
38	3.3	130	54.4
42	5.6	135	57.2
46.4	8	140	60
50	10	145	62.8
55	12.8	150	65.6
60	15.6	155	68.3
65	18.3	160	71.1
70	21.1	165	73.9
75	23.9	170	76.7
80	26.7	175	79.4
85	29.4	180	82.2
90	32.2	185	85
95	35	190	87.8
100	37.8	195	90.6
105	40.6	200	93.3
110	43.3	205	96.1
115	46.1	210	98.9
120	48.9	212	100

To convert Fahrenheit degrees into Centigrade, subtract 32, multiply by 5 and divide by 9. To convert Centigrade into Fahrenheit, multiply by 9, divide by 5 and add 32.

INDEX

Additional photography:

© Rick Doyle p. 64–65
© Shelley Seccombe p. 90–91